TRAINING FOR A LIFESTYLE OF

LIVING
from the
UNSEEN
reflections from a transformed life

Wendy Backlund

© copyright 2015 Wendy Backlund, Igniting Hope Ministries

wendybacklund.com

ignitinghope.com

Acknowledgements

Cover: Lorraine Box, Linda Lee

Inside Design: Julie Heth, Robert Schwendenmann

Editing: Melissa Amato, Megan Cotton, Darlene Edskerud, Autumn Elliott, Julia Graham, Julie Heth

Special Writing Assistance: Autumn Elliott

Videographers: Joshua Bailey, Sam Kim, JR McGee

Video Editor: Katy Andres

Video Manufacturing: Bethel Media

Small Group Members: Cyndi Barber, Lorraine Box, Holly Hayes, Julie Heth, Elisabeth King, Joellah Lutz, Amy McConathy, Anita McGee, Julie Mustard, Elizabeth Reisinger, Katrina Stevenson

ISBN: 978-0-9863094-2-7

TABLE OF CONTENTS

Note from the Author   vii
Chapter Components   ix
How to Use This Video Series   xi
Spirit Awareness Assessment   xiii
Introductory Lesson   2
Video: Introduction   **4**

First Reflection   *Living from the Spirit*   7
Substance of the Unseen   8
Train Your Brain   10
Hearing from Our Spirit   12
Our Supernatural Identity   14
Accessing the Kingdom   16
Video: First Reflection   **18**

Second Reflection   *Limitless Reception*   21
The Power of a Blessing   22
The Power of Light   24
Learning to Receive: Part One   26
Learning to Receive: Part Two   28
Video: Second Reflection   **30**

Third Reflection   *Abundant Living*   33
Life More Abundant   34
Inner Unity   36
Creating Positive Strongholds   38
Supernatural Laws   40
Mysteries of the Kingdom   42
Video: Third Reflection   **44**

Fourth Reflection   *Godly Imaginations*   47
Fix Your Eye   48
Dimensions of the Mind: Part One   50
Dimensions of the Mind: Part Two   52
Attaching Faith   54
Video: Fourth Reflection   **56**
What Now? The Journey Continues   59
Spirit Awareness Assessment   61
Living from the Unseen Declarations   63
Additional Resources   65

NOTE
FROM THE AUTHOR

This workbook, with the videos, is a five-part study based on my book, *Living from the Unseen*. This practical tool holds keys to unlocking revelation that has dramatically changed my life and perspective. The revelations I have received through my own journey have not changed my theology as much as they have given life and manifestation to the beliefs I already embraced.

For many years my life did not measure up with my theology and I thought there was something uniquely wrong with me. I thought I was the exception to the promises and statements of what a believer looked like. My perception of what a "good Christian" looked like seemed heavy, hard, and impossible! I had a powerful encounter with Christ in the 1970s, but by the late '80s I was simply going through the motions, trying to please God by works and tears. By the time renewal hit in the '90s, I was ready for change! For many, the renewal was a time of fresh encounters and supernatural signs and wonders. For me, it was a time of life-altering revelations. I had not realized how much of the Word was only a mental assent of truth for me, rather than an experience of abundant life and victory.

I created this study to help others discover what a resurrected lifestyle looks like and give them a path for passionately pursuing a supernatural life. **I encourage you to take the Spirit Awareness Assessment on my website (wendybacklund.com) before you begin this study and then again after you complete it to assess how much you've grown.**

May we become aware of the spiritual realities and principles affecting our everyday lives. May we go beyond awareness of attack and evil influence and step into the reality of a more powerful influence – the influence of the unseen Kingdom of God. Living from the unseen, through the eyes of our spirit, will move us from having a theology into an experience of living a resurrected life.

Blessings,
Wendy Backlund

CHAPTER COMPONENTS

Reflections

Take time to sit and meditate on what God highlighted to you while you were reading the assigned chapter from Wendy's book, *Living from the Unseen*. Consider the following questions as you make notes in this section: How did it make you feel? What impacted your spirit? Did you have any sense you were supposed to dig deeper? Did you receive any further revelation?

Questions

Asking questions invites God to give you answers. If we don't ask why or how about certain things, we won't know the answers. This section will help you dig deeper into key points in the chapter and go a step further in shifting your mindset.

Declarations

Proverbs 18:21 says, "Life and death are in the power of the tongue." What we speak is so important. We get to partner with God when we declare goodness over ourselves. Faith comes by hearing (Romans 10:17). When we speak life, we can hear it and have faith to believe it. Declarations will help you create good beliefs throughout this journey. This section of the workbook also provides room for you to add your own declarations to speak over yourself. Make a list of declarations and speak them over yourself multiple times during your devotional time and throughout your day.

Application

This section provides an opportunity for you to apply what you are learning to your daily life. Through these applications, we are training our spirits to be prominent over our souls and bodies.

Imagination

Exercise your imagination under the anointing of the Holy Spirit. Intentionally give God the right to use your imagination so it can be used for its intended purpose. See pages 91-95 of *Living from the Unseen* for a more detailed explanation of intentionally using our gift of imagination in a healthy way.

Journal

Take time to journal throughout the week about how the application in each section affected you.

HOW TO USE
THIS TRAINING MATERIAL

The *Living from the Unseen* training includes Wendy's *Living from the Unseen* book, this workbook, and a corresponding video series. Each of these contain unique material and are designed to be used together. While this training is perfect for individual study, we highly recommend completing it in a small group setting to maximize your experience and build community in the process. Before you begin your training, take the Spiritual Awareness Assessment (learn more on page xiii) to track your growth.

Recommendations for Group Study:

1. Read assigned reflections in *Living from the Unseen* on your own.
2. Answer the corresponding questions in this workbook on your own.
3. Watch the corresponding video as a group (not including the soaking time).
4. Discuss your responses to the workbook questions as a group.
5. Watch the remainder of the video (Wendy's guided soaking session) as a group.
6. Finish by discussing your experiences as a group.

Ideas for Conducting Small Groups: Although Wendy's study was designed to be completed according to the steps above, we encourage groups to be creative and use this workbook, the videos, and soaking excercises in whatever way best fits your group.

How to Lead Video Series Time:

During each video, there is a 20 minute teaching, a break, then a ten minute guided soaking session. We recommend that before you do the soaking, take time to discuss the video as a group and go over the workbook responses. When it is time for soaking, encourage people to get comfortable and ask that they do not move around or become a distraction to others.

After your soaking time, plan time for sharing as a group. This is a powerful part of the study that should not be passed over lightly. **Leaders,** ask what people saw, heard, or felt during the soaking. Stress that we do not have to understand what we see or hear – the goal is to first hear and see from the Spirit, like a baby learning to understand the language of their parents.

SPIRITUAL AWARENESS ASSESSMENT

Take the Assessment

To best assess your current spirit awareness as you begin this journey, log on to:
http://wendybacklund.com/spirit-awareness-assessment and take Wendy's Spirit Awareness Assessment.*

Pre-Training Assessment Score

After completing the online assessment, record the date and your score below.

Spirit Awareness Assessment Score: _____

Date: _____

Post-Training Assessment Score

Once you have completed this workbook, the *Living from the Unseen* book, and the video series, we recommend returning to the link above and taking the Spirit Awareness Assessment again to track your growth. Then, record your new score below (page 61 at the end of this workbook will also prompt you to take the assessment again and record your post-training score here). There is endless growth available in the Spirit!

Spirit Awareness Assessment Score: _____

Date: _____

Ongoing Training

We recommend consistently reading portions of this workbook that the Spirit highlights to you to accelerate the process of renewing your mind and changing the way you see life. For instance, listening to or reading certain revelatory messages multiple times a day for a period of time can assist your spirit in receiving truth; it's a matter of helping the message by-pass your intellect and enter your spirit.

*Adapted from Rev. Dr. Donna Cox Assessment

INTRODUCTION

"We must discover what a resurrected life looks like and then passionately pursue that supernatural way of life."
—Wendy Backlund

INTRODUCTORY LESSON

Reflections

Read pages ix-xiii in *Living from the Unseen*. What are your goals for this study? What areas do you want to experience growth in?

_____

_____

Questions

On page x, I mention our need to move from a theology of our spirit nature to a clear awareness of our spirit and its potential.

Question 1: What do you think our spirit is able to do that our flesh cannot?

_____

_____

_____

Question 2: What do you think are the spiritual resources available to us? Can our natural mind and body access them without our spirit?

_____

_____

_____

Declarations We have provided one declaration betlow. Create two more personal declarations you would like to speak over yourself.

I am more spirit than flesh.

_____

_____

Application

Be more aware of your spirit today. Notice how it wants to respond and what it wants to believe in particular situations. For example, if you have an intimidating job to do, check with your spirit. What is it believing? How does it feel? Does it feel fearful or does it feel confident?

_____

_____

_____

Imagination

Picture yourself as more spirit than body. Ask the Holy Spirit to help you see the reality of the spirit realm and what your spirit can access to gain breakthrough in your life. Dream about what could be possible if you bring the Kingdom of Light into your current or daily situations. Record your revelation below.

_____

_____

_____

Journal

Write below how the above application affected your week.

_____

_____

_____

_____

_____

_____

_____

_____

Video – *Introduction*

Watch Wendy's Introduction video and take notes below.

Video Notes

Soaking Notes

First Reflection

LIVING FROM THE SPIRIT

"We must have a revelation of our identity as new creatures, a new race of beings, born of the Spirit. If we can become more aware of that part of ourselves and allow it to have a voice, then we will begin to see what walking in the Spirit can look like."

—Wendy Backlund

SUBSTANCE OF
THE UNSEEN

Reflections

What did God say to you through pages 1-8 in *Living from the Unseen*?

_____

_____

_____

Questions

On pages 4 and 5, I talk about our spirits expanding and contracting under certain circumstances.

Question 1: When are some times you have experienced your spirit expanding or contracting?

_____

_____

_____

Question 2: What thoughts and beliefs were affecting your spirit in each of these situations?

_____

_____

_____

Declarations Add two personal declarations you would like to speak over yourself.

The substance of God's love and peace overwhelms people everywhere I go.

_____

_____

Application

Train yourself to be more aware of your spirit by taking note of how you are affected in different venues. Instead of being a victim to the prevailing spirit, consciously picture yourself carrying the presence of God and emanating His grace, love, and peace. Watch and look for physical reactions to the Presence you carry.

_____

_____

Imagination

Spend time picturing yourself carrying the powerful presence of God. Think of powerful people who have affected you just by being in their presence, and see and feel yourself having that same influence because you are a carrier of His presence. What happened when you consciously pictured yourself carrying the Presence and emanating His grace, love, and peace?

_____

_____

_____

Journal

Write below how the above application affected your week.

_____

_____

_____

_____

_____

_____

TRAIN YOUR BRAIN

Reflections

What did God say to you through pages 9-13 in *Living from the Unseen*?

_____

_____

_____

Questions

I write on page 11, "Unless we expect to see and hear from the unseen realm, then our experience will be limited to our limited expectations."

Question 1: How much do you expect to see, hear, or experience the unseen realm everyday?

_____

_____

_____

Question 2: What are some things you can do to remind yourself you are not just a physical body and that you live in the midst of a supernatural realm?

_____

_____

_____

Declarations   Add two personal declarations you would like to speak over yourself.

My spirit is arising within me. I can feel it, and I can hear it! _____

_____

_____

Application

Consider an area of your life that has become boring or passionless. Ask God what that area will look like once impacted by the supernatural. Allow God to set you back on the journey of learning to walk according to the Spirit in that area of your life.

_____

_____

_____

Imagination

As with any new skill, we need to take time and energy to practice being aware of the unseen realm. Ask the Father to show you what is going on around you in the unseen realm. Where are the angels? What do they look like? Is there anything else in the room, including colors or lights? Do not be afraid of making it up. You won't be teaching or starting a new doctrine from what you see. Simply use this time to practice seeing and trust Him to confirm and strengthen your ability to see as you practice with the Holy Spirit.

_____

_____

_____

Journal

Write below about how the above application affected your week.

_____

_____

_____

_____

_____

_____

HEARING FROM OUR SPIRIT

Reflections

What did God say to you through pages 15-19 in *Living from the Unseen*?

_____

_____

_____

Questions

On page 18, I state that my goal is to trust what my spirit is saying as equally as I trust my natural sight, hearing, smell, or touch.

Question 1: Have you ever felt or known something, but did not understand how you knew it? Give an example.

_____

_____

_____

Question 2: What lies are keeping you from believing you can see and hear with your spirit?

_____

_____

_____

Declarations Add two personal declarations you would like to speak over yourself.

My brain hears and responds easily to the voice of my spirit.

_____

_____

Application

Before your day or week begins, ask the Holy Spirit for thoughts that will apply to your day or week and write them down to compare with how the actual day or week plays out. Ask God to teach you to hear Him more clearly and expect to have fun during the process. He is not a harsh teacher.

_____

_____

_____

Imagination

Imagine yourself going to a spiritual gym everyday and working out your spiritual ability to see and hear from your spirit. Picture what you can do with spiritually strong and healthy eyes and ears. What would you possibly see and hear that you were not able to see and hear before? Remember there are no right or wrong answers.

_____

_____

_____

Journal

Write below about how the above application affected your week.

_____

_____

_____

_____

_____

_____

OUR SUPERNATURAL IDENTITY

Reflections

What did God say to you through pages 21-24 in *Living from the Unseen*?

_____

_____

_____

Questions

On page 22, I state, "Too many believers try to determine their identity from their past failures or experiences rather than from their new birth."

Question 1: In what ways have you used your past experiences to validate or define your identity, rather than God's Word?

_____

_____

_____

Question 2: In what way has that limited your ability to live from or demonstrate your supernatural identity?

_____

_____

_____

Declarations Add two personal declarations you would like to speak over yourself.

I am a partaker of the divine nature, and I look like my Father.

_____

_____

Application

Write down some new identity declarations that line up with your new birth status. As you do this, consider who your Daddy really is and what He is able to do. Write your thoughts below.

_____

_____

_____

Imagination

Take time to imagine your old self dying with Christ and becoming a new resurrected supernatural being. Identify with this new creation. Picture Father God beside you. Imagine your resurrected self learning to interact with the world, like a toddler interacts with its new world (see page 22). What did Daddy show you?

_____

_____

_____

Journal

Write below about how the above application affected your week.

_____

_____

_____

_____

_____

_____

_____

_____

ACCESSING THE KINGDOM

Reflections

What did God say to you through pages 25-28 in *Living from the Unseen*?

_____

_____

_____

Questions

In this lesson, I say that Christians tend to believe we become disciples by acting like Jesus rather than believing like Him. In other words, people are trying to *act* like something they do not *believe* they are. This becomes simply a performance, rather than a re-creation.

Question 1: What areas of "becoming a disciple" have been difficult and stressful? In what areas of your life are you "acting" like Jesus rather than believing like Jesus?

_____

_____

_____

Question 2: What has Jesus called you to believe? What are ways you can start believing like Him? Take note of how you feel when you believe you *are* something versus how you feel when you are *trying* to be something you do not believe you are.

_____

_____

_____

Declarations Add one personal declaration you would like to speak over yourself.

I anticipate good coming my way.

Goodness and mercy follow me all the days of my life.

_____

Application

Instead of asking God what to do today, ask Him what He wants you to believe today.

_____

_____

_____

Imagination

Imagine what it feels like to have a belief that your identity is what enables you to do impossible things. Instead of picturing yourself *acting* like you are supernatural, picture what you would do if you *believed* you were supernatural.

_____

_____

_____

Journal

Write below about how the above application affected your week.

_____

_____

_____

_____

_____

_____

_____

_____

Video – *First Reflection*

Watch the First Reflection video and take notes below.

Video Notes

Soaking Notes

Second Reflection

LIMITLESS RECEPTION

"Deception distorts perception,
and distorted perception limits our reception!"
—Wendy Backlund

THE POWER OF A
BLESSING

Reflections

What did God say to you through pages 29-35 in *Living from the Unseen*?

_____

_____

_____

Questions

On page 32, I write, "Many are still living an Old Testament experience even though we are equipped through the cross to bring life and healing everywhere that the curse has brought death and destruction."

Question 1: In what area or areas of your life have you accepted the curse of fallen man and not taken authority to bring blessing, life, and redemption?

_____

_____

_____

Question 2: Why do you think some people have more belief in the power of a witch's curse than in the power of a Christian's blessing?

_____

_____

_____

Declarations Add two personal declarations you would like to speak over yourself.

I bless my descendants with wisdom, love, prosperity, and peace in every area of their lives.

_____

_____

_____

Application

Take time to imagine the power of a blessing. Make a list of people or places you want to bless and proclaim specific blessings over, such as success, peace, favor, and joy.

Imagination

Imagine what witches look like cursing people or regions. Then imagine a group of Christians blessing someone or a region. Picture how much more powerful a blessing is and see it overriding all curses.

Journal

Write below about how the above application affected your week.

THE POWER
OF LIGHT

Reflections

What did God say to you through pages 37-41 in *Living from the Unseen*?

_____

_____

_____

Questions

On page 39, I mention the concept that Christians being light is not just a symbolic thought, but an actual substance that affects atmospheres, lives, and the spirit realm.

Question 1: Do you have more faith in your performance or abilities than in the weight and authority of the light of Christ in you? Share an example of when Christ's light in you or someone you know made a difference in a situation.

_____

_____

_____

Question 2: Share an example of when you tried to do something for God as a physical being, out of your own strength, instead of as a light from God, empowered by the Spirit. How did it make you feel?

_____

_____

_____

Declarations   Add two personal declarations you would like to speak over yourself.

The light of God dwells in me and destroys the works of the enemy.

_____

_____

Application

Today, let the powerful light in you affect a circumstance or person you encounter. Allow it to overcome sickness, blind eyes, hopelessness, despair, or whatever is needed in the moment.

_____

_____

_____

Imagination

Imagine yourself full of light shining with the glory of God. The light is love, power, wisdom, and joy. Picture yourself carrying the Kingdom in such brilliance that it establishes authority to bring people into His presence.

_____

_____

_____

Journal

Write below about how the above application affected your week.

_____

_____

_____

_____

_____

_____

_____

_____

_____

_____

LEARNING TO RECEIVE: PART 1

Reflections

What did God say to you through pages 43-46 in *Living from the Unseen*?

_____

_____

_____

Questions

On page 44, I write, "I unconsciously kept my success at my perceived level of worth or value." Hence, blessings were only for consistent good performance.

Question 1: Is there an area in your life where you have lost all or most of your hope for breakthrough because of your past failures or performance? Write it below.

_____

_____

_____

Question 2: How can you posture yourself to receive your breakthrough?

_____

_____

_____

Declarations   Add two personal declarations you would like to speak over yourself.

I easily rest and receive in His presence.

_____

_____

Application

Spend some time waiting in God's presence. Pretend to be a handkerchief and soak up His love and anointing. For more tools on soaking, visit wendybacklund.com.

_____

_____

_____

Imagination

Picture yourself receiving something you do not think you deserve. Let yourself feel the emotion and results of receiving it.

_____

_____

_____

Journal

Write below about how the above application affected your week.

_____

_____

_____

_____

_____

_____

_____

_____

LEARNING TO RECEIVE: PART 2

Reflections

What did God say to you through pages 47-50 in *Living from the Unseen*?

_____

_____

_____

Questions

On page 48, I talk about receiving from imperfect people so we can glean from their strengths and honor the talents they do have. Weakness in certain areas does not nullify our strength in other areas.

Question 1: Why do you think we struggle with receiving from imperfect people?

_____

_____

_____

Question 2: How would you feel if people dishonored your gifts because you were not perfected in other areas of your life?

_____

_____

_____

Declarations   Add two personal declarations you would like to speak over yourself.

I see and draw out the gold in people.

_____

_____

Application

Today as you go out, if you encounter anyone you disagree with or see a weakness in, posture yourself to receive something from them.

_____

_____

_____

Imagination

Ask Holy Spirit to help you imagine what greatness lies within someone you previously had no expressed honor or value for.

_____

_____

_____

Journal

Write below about how the above application affected your week.

_____

_____

_____

_____

_____

_____

_____

_____

Video – *Second Reflection*

Video Notes

Soaking Notes

Third Reflection

ABUNDANT LIVING

"One of the greatest revelations of this generation is the understanding that the Kingdom of Heaven is a present tense reality for all believers."

–Wendy Backlund

LIFE MORE ABUNDANT

Reflections

What did God say to you through pages 51-57 in *Living from the Unseen*?

_____

_____

_____

Questions

On page 54, I ask if you spend more time trying "not" to do certain things or if your focus is on releasing the divine nature within you.

Questions 1: Why do you think religion focuses on stopping something instead of becoming something?

_____

_____

_____

Question 2: Who do you want to become?

_____

_____

_____

Declarations Add two personal declarations you would like to speak over yourself.

God wants me to live fully and use the talents that bring energy and fulfillment to my life.

_____

_____

_____

Application

Write down three things you enjoy doing. How can you glorify God through them? Write down who you want to be – not titles or positions, but personality, gifts, or talents. For example, I thought I desired to be musical because I loved to worship. I did not become passionate enough to learn to sing or play an instrument, but I did spend a lot of time in His presence and realized it was not the playing or singing that was my real goal, but the worship!

_____

_____

_____

Imagination

Imagine yourself as God sees you in the future. Picture yourself already living in freedom and power. Whatever you have seen as a stumbling block to your destiny, see yourself already free from it and setting others free also.

_____

_____

_____

Journal

Write below about how the above application affected your week.

_____

_____

_____

_____

_____

_____

_____

INNER UNITY

Reflections

What did God say to you through pages 59-62 in *Living from the Unseen*?

_____

_____

_____

Questions

On page 61, I talk about realizing the difference between what we want to believe and what our unconscious mind or heart really believes.

Question 1: Identify some areas of disunity within yourself.

_____

_____

_____

Question 2: Can you think of some wrong conclusions you have made about yourself because of a past experience?

_____

_____

_____

Declarations   Add two personal declarations you would like to speak over yourself.

I submit my mind, will, and emotions to the truth of God's Word, which says I am altogether beautiful and beloved by God.

_____

Application

What do you think holds you back from breaking out of your normal level of success in areas of your life such as finances, relationships, jobs, and spiritual growth? Ask God to reveal any false conclusions made in your past that are holding you to your present experience. Create declarations that will help change your beliefs. You might want to check and see if your words, emotions, thoughts, and prayers are in unity.

_____

_____

_____

Imagination

Picture God making healthy statements about you. Give Him time to give you some healthy identity statements about yourself.

_____

_____

_____

Journal

Write below about how the above application affected your week.

_____

_____

_____

_____

_____

_____

_____

_____

CREATING POSITIVE STRONGHOLDS

Reflections

What did God say to you through pages 63-67 in *Living from the Unseen*?

_____

_____

_____

Questions

Page 64 explores the difference between constantly battling to believe right things versus building new strongholds so the battle is no longer necessary.

Question 1: Identify a new stronghold you would like to build so that the constant battle can be eliminated.

_____

_____

_____

Question 2: What is the difference between subduing an emotion and building a new stronghold?

_____

_____

_____

Declarations Add two personal declarations you would like to speak over yourself.

My new strongholds are making life easy.

_____

_____

_____

Application

What emotion do you continually have to subdue in order for it to line up with the truth? Write the belief governing the emotion, and put it inside a covered jar as a prophetic act. Then write the truth and begin declaring, meditating, and receiving revelation for this new chosen stronghold.

_____

_____

_____

Imagination

Once we create new positive strongholds, there will be evidence in our lives by how we react to circumstances or situations we face. What would life look like under your new belief?

_____

_____

_____

Journal

Write below about how the above application affected your week.

_____

_____

_____

_____

_____

_____

_____

_____

SUPERNATURAL LAWS

Reflections

What did God say to you through pages 69-73 in *Living from the Unseen*?

_____

_____

_____

Questions

On pages 70-71, I discuss how vital it is to understand how the unseen realm works and what spiritual laws (like the natural law of gravity in the seen realm) are at work in our lives.

Question 1: What spiritual laws can you start focusing on to supersede natural consequences of life? For example, sowing and reaping, law of grace and life, power of light over darkness, and power of life over death.

_____

_____

_____

Question 2: Have you ever been aware of a blessing that was related to something you had sown in the past? Explain.

_____

_____

_____

Declarations Add two personal declarations you would like to speak over yourself.

I have great revelation on how the laws of the spirit realm work.

_____

_____

Application

Think about an area of your life that consistently seems untouched by God's grace. Ask God if there is a spiritual law at work that is hindering breakthrough in this area. Do not seek to hear out of fear, but believe that He will give you the wisdom you need. Rest and listen with peaceful expectation. Believe that He awakens your ear to hear Him (Isaiah 50:5).

_____

_____

_____

Imagination

Imagine the power of spiritual laws you have sown in your life beginning to overtake you and bless you a hundredfold. Imagine a harvest for things sown being multiplied to you.

_____

_____

_____

Journal

Write below about how the above application affected your week.

_____

_____

_____

_____

_____

_____

_____

_____

MYSTERIES OF THE KINGDOM

Reflections

What did God say to you through pages 75-79 in *Living from the Unseen*?

_____

_____

_____

Questions

Page 78 says, "When we attach faith to His promises, then we can factor those promises into our circumstances and come up with new possible results for impossible circumstances."

Question 1: What are some signs that we have not attached faith to a circumstance?

_____

_____

_____

Question 2: How would the outcome of a situation look different if you believed His promises over the facts?

_____

_____

_____

Declarations Add two personal declarations you would like to speak over yourself.

I have unseen resources and spiritual blessings to overcome every negative circumstance.

_____

_____

_____

Application

Look at an impossible circumstance through the eyes of your spirit. What are some promises that can be applied to the circumstance? Declare these promises over your circumstances.

_____

_____

_____

Imagination

Imagine how the unseen power of His promises is affecting your life and circumstances. Feel the confidence of knowing He is bigger than circumstances and He is well able to overcome them!

_____

_____

_____

Journal

Write below about how the above application affected your week.

_____

_____

_____

_____

_____

_____

_____

_____

_____

Video – *Third Reflection*

Video Notes

Soaking Notes

GODLY IMAGINATIONS

"Our imagination is the womb for the seed of either God's Word or satan's thoughts."

–Wendy Backlund

FIX YOUR EYES

Reflections

What did God say to you through pages 81-86 in *Living from the Unseen*?

_____

_____

_____

Questions

On page 84, I quote a psychologist who said that when the will and the imagination are in conflict, the imagination always wins.

Question 1: How have you viewed the imagination? What are new ways you will start using your imagination (e.g. dreams, finances, jobs, relationships)?

_____

_____

_____

Question 2: Why do you think the past has so much influence over our present?

_____

_____

_____

Declarations Add two personal declarations you would like to speak over yourself.

The eyes of my imagination are enlightened to see the glorious inheritance and power I have been given.

_____

Application

Is there anything you have the will to do or to quit, but can't see or imagine yourself having victory? Do you keep rehearsing your failure? Take a moment to recognize what you are seeing or feeling when you attempt to change and then adjust accordingly.

_____

_____

_____

Imagination

Spend some time imagining a successful future. Imagine not only what you do, but who you are. Imagine yourself as always victorious, overcoming, powerful, wise, and successful. Make success your identity, not an accomplishment.

_____

_____

_____

Journal

Write below about how the above application affected your week.

_____

_____

_____

_____

_____

_____

_____

DIMENSIONS OF THE MIND: PART 1

Reflections

What did God say to you through pages 87-90 in *Living from the Unseen*?

_____

_____

_____

Questions

Page 88 expounds on how our thoughts can either motivate and strengthen us or discourage and weaken us.

Question 1: What are some recurring thoughts that lead you to discouragement or hopelessness?

_____

_____

_____

Question 2: Knowing that God is a God of hope, what thoughts would God want you to have?

_____

_____

_____

Declarations Add two personal declarations you would like to speak over yourself.

I succeed in everything I put my hand to.

_____

_____

_____

Application

Build an altar today around a successful past experience that reveals how God has changed you or helped you. Create a journal of successes. Celebrate seemingly small things like saying no to cake, speaking well of someone, declaring God's Word, or praying for ten minutes.

Imagination

Imagine the happy thoughts God has about you. Let Him paint a picture in your mind of your future under His power and resources.

Journal

Write below about how the above application affected your week.

DIMENSIONS OF THE MIND: PART 2

Reflections

What did God say to you through pages 91-95 in *Living from the Unseen*?

_____

_____

_____

Questions

On page 93, I make the comment that babies instinctively know they should not base their potential on their past, but on their parents.

Question 1: In what areas do you need to look at your Father to discover how powerful you are? What would you be practicing or attempting to do after watching Him?

_____

_____

_____

Question 2: If you really believed "the same Spirit that raised Christ from the dead dwells in you" (Ephesians 1:19-20), how would that affect sickness in you or in someone else? How would that affect your tiredness or depression? How would that affect your city?

_____

_____

_____

Declarations Add two personal declarations you would like to speak over yourself.

I know my past, but I imagine my future according to the power that works in me.

_____

_____

Application

Ask Holy Spirit to highlight one aspect of God's character to you. Then imagine how you could have had a different result in a past experience if you had been convinced you have the same DNA as your Father. Now picture yourself walking in your Heavenly Father's DNA until that picture eclipses your past experience.

_____

_____

_____

Imagination

Imagine yourself as a baby spirit watching Father God and being convinced that you are made in His image.

_____

_____

_____

Journal

Write below about how the above application affected your week.

_____

_____

_____

_____

_____

_____

_____

_____

_____

_____

ATTACHING FAITH

Reflections

What did God say to you through pages 97-101 in *Living from the Unseen*?

_____

_____

_____

Questions

On page 97, I say, "I do not need to do anything different, I just need to attach great faith to what I am already doing."

Question 1: Name something you regularly do that you could attach great faith to so it can produce supernatural results rather than only natural results.

_____

_____

_____

Question 2: What do you think life looks like when it is subject to the Kingdom of God?

_____

_____

_____

Declarations Add two personal declarations you would like to speak over yourself.

I attach great faith to everything I do; therefore, everything I do creates life and change.

_____

_____

Application

Write down some simple things you do every day and dream with God about the powerful effects these things can have because of Christ living in you. Write down some declarations based on what God shows you concerning these things.

_____

_____

_____

Imagination

Imagine great and powerful things happening in situations that didn't used to have any significance or power.

_____

_____

_____

Journal

Write below about how the above application affected your week.

_____

_____

_____

_____

_____

_____

_____

_____

Video – *Fourth Reflection*

Video Notes

Soaking Notes

WHAT NOW?
CONTINUING THE
JOURNEY

Although this study has come to a close, I know your journey has only begun. Jesus said, "For whoever has, to him more will be given" (Mark 4:25). **This holds true for wisdom and revelation: the more understanding we receive, the more will be given.** Each new truth becomes a launching pad for the next, higher revelation we can receive, as we build "precept upon precept, line upon line" (Isaiah 28:10). I bless you with eyes to see the unseen realities of the Kingdom. **My prayer is that this workbook will lead you into even greater truths that in turn benefit the whole body of Christ.** Now that you have finished the study, please return to my website and take the assessment again. This is one way you can begin to track and celebrate your growth.

The things shared in this workbook were not revelations I received in a single day that instantly bore fruit. I had to consistently apply these revelations, but more importantly, I had to make them my new lens for viewing life. **Through a lifestyle of speaking declarations and meditating, I was able to establish these truths into the spirit of my mind.** At first, it can be hard to challenge your old beliefs and feelings, but I encourage you to keep going. It will get easier!

I believe consistently rereading portions of this workbook the Spirit highlights to you will accelerate the process of renewing your mind and change the way you see life. It is not enough for your intellect to understand something. You must actively engage your spirit to ground these truths within it. For instance, I will often listen to certain revelatory messages five times a day so the truth goes past my intellect and into my spirit. **The goal is to understand and believe with the spirit of your mind.**

When reading, listening, or seeing something that causes your spirit to leap, I encourage you to search it out. Spend time meditating on it and asking God questions. Recognize that your spirit is trying to teach your brain something. I hope you will be challenged by questions in this workbook that cause your spirit to leap and your mind to be renewed, so your life will be transformed.

By the grace of God, I declare this study will be a catalyst for opening blind eyes. In the name of Jesus, I impart fresh grace for you to live from the unseen realm and I pray for His Kingdom to manifest more fully in your life.

Blessings on your journey,
Wendy

"But God has revealed them to us through His Spirit. For the Spirit searches all things, yes, the deep things of God. For what man knows the things of a man except the spirit of the man which is in him?"
(1 Corinthians 2:10-11a NKJV)

SPIRIT AWARENESS ASSESSMENT

Return to **http://wendybacklund.com/spirit-awareness-assessment** and take Wendy's Spirit Awareness Assessment again to track your growth. Then, turn to **page xiii** of this workbook and record your post-training assessment score along with the date.

We encourage you to read sections of this workbook and Wendy's book again, and rewatch the video series to accelerate the process of renewing your mind.

Blessings on your ongoing journey to live more fully from your spirit!

LIVING FROM THE UNSEEN DECLARATIONS

1. I am more spirit than flesh (Galatians 5:25).

2. The substance of God's love and peace overwhelms people everywhere I go (1 John 4:4).

3. My spirit is arising within me. I can feel it, and I can hear it (Ephesians 2:4-6).

4. My brain hears and responds easily to the voice of my spirit (John 10:27).

5. I am a partaker of the divine nature and I look like my Father (2 Peter 1:4).

6. I anticipate good coming my way (Psalm 118:24).

7. Goodness and mercy follow me all the days of my life (Psalm 23:6).

8. I bless my descendants with wisdom, love, prosperity, and peace in every area of their lives (Proverbs 11:11).

9. The light of God dwells in me and destroys the works of the enemy (Matthew 5:14).

10. I easily rest and receive in His presence (John 20:21-22).

11. I see and draw out the gold in people (2 Corinthians 5:16).

12. I believe God wants me to use the talents He has given me that bring energy and fulfillment to my life (John 10:10).

13. I submit my mind, will, and emotions to the truth of God's Word (Romans 12:2).

14. New strongholds are making life easy (1 Corinthians 10:4-5).

15. I have great revelation on how the laws of the spirit realm work (Romans 8:1).

16. I have unseen resources and spiritual blessings to overcome every negative circumstance (Philippians 4:19).

17. The eyes of my imagination are enlightened to see the glorious inheritance and power that I have been called into (Ephesians 1:18-19).

18. I succeed in everything I put my hand to (Philippians 4:13).

19. I know my past, but I imagine my future according to the power that works in me (Ephesians 3:20).

20. I attach great faith to everything I do; therefore, everything I do creates life and change (Romans 4:20-21).

For more information on Wendy, to view her speaking itinerary, or for additional resources, visit wendybacklund.com.

For additional resources from Steve and Wendy Backlund, Igniting Hope Ministries, Bethel Church, or Global Legacy, visit the following websites:

ignitinghope.com
ibethel.org
globallegacy.com

Made in United States
Troutdale, OR
01/16/2025

27991267R00046